RON

A Startright Elf

Baby Book

Baby's Busy Day

By Debby Slier
Illustrated by Cathy Beylon

ENGLAND

Printed in Great Britain.

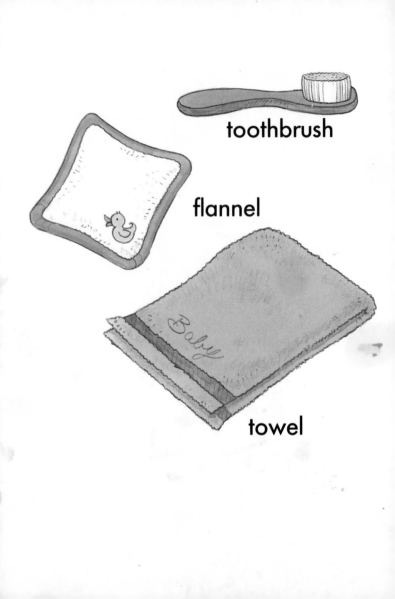

toothbrush

flannel

towel

washing

shoes

socks

pants

dressing

cup

spoon

bowl of cereal

eating

toy

ball

teddy bear

baby walker

playing

puppy

push-chair

walking

teddy bear

puppy

friends

car

baby's car seat

travelling

shopping
trolley

money

purse

shopping

bath toy

soap

towel

flannel

bath

bathtime

teddy bear

books

reading

cot

teddy bear

pillow

blanket